NEMO·ME·IMPUNE·LACESSIT

The Early Christian & Pictish
Monuments of Scotland

An illustrated introduction,
with illustrated and descriptive catalogues of the,
Meigle and St. Vigeans Collections

by

STEWART CRUDEN, F.S.A., A.R.I.B.A.

Inspector of Ancient Monuments for Scotland

EDINBURGH

HER MAJESTY'S STATIONERY OFFICE

1964

D1363904

© *Crown Copyright* 1964

Published by
HER MAJESTY'S STATIONERY OFFICE

To be purchased from
13A Castle Street, Edinburgh 2
York House, Kingsway, London W.C.2
423 Oxford Street, London W.1
109 St. Mary Street, Cardiff
39 King Street, Manchester 2
50 Fairfax Street, Bristol 1
35 Smallbrook, Ringway, Birmingham 3
80 Chichester Street, Belfast
or through any bookseller

Price 5s. 0d. net

First Published 1957
Second Edition 1964

Frontispiece: The Meigle Museum.

A Warning to Theorists

'In the church-yard of Glamis[1] is a stone similar to those at Aberlemni.
This is supposed to have been erected in memory of the assassination of
King Malcolm, and is called his grave-stone. On one front is a cross; on
the upper part is some wild beast, and opposite to it a centaur: beneath,
in one compartment, is the head of a wolf; these animals denoting the
barbarity of the conspirators: in another compartment are two persons
shaking hands; in their other hand is a battle-axe: perhaps these are
represented in the act of confederacy. On the opposite front of the stone
are represented an eel and another fish. This alludes to the fate of the
murderers, who, as soon as they had committed the horrid act, fled.
The roads were at that time covered with snow; they lost the path, and
went on to the lake of Forfar, which happened at the time to be frozen
over, but not sufficiently strong to bear their weight: the ice broke, and
they all perished miserably.'

THOMAS PENNANT

A Tour in Scotland, 1776, Vol II.　173

---

[1] The Glamis Stone, plates 5 and 6.

Preface to the second edition

Since the first edition was published the Ministry of Public Building and Works has re-housed the St. Vigeans collection in a new museum. An illustrated catalogue of these monuments has now been added to this book. The item numbers in the catalogue are those of Romilly Allen and Anderson's great work *The Early Christian Monuments of Scotland*. The numbering of the stones in the Meigle catalogue has been changed to this generally accepted system of reference. A few titles have been added to the Bibliography.

Contents

Illustrations

(Grouped at the back of the book, following page 28)

The block used for Plate 13 is the property of the Society of Antiquaries of Scotland and is used with their kind permission. Plate 25 is reproduced by kind permission of Mrs. Helen O'Neil, FSA. The animal on the front cover is a Burghead Bull, recurrent in Moray but not elsewhere.

6

The Historical Background

IN the early years of the 5th century the Roman legions were withdrawn from Britain to stiffen resistance at the heart of their threatened Empire and the British were cut off from the civilisation to which they had belonged for more than 300 years. Their appeals for help were unanswered; they were left to defend themselves. Land-hungry barbarians, once held in check by the legions and the navy, moved in to seize the spoils of a rich and peaceful land. Behind the first invaders others followed. Across the Channel the Angles, Saxons and Jutes invaded the eastern shores; across the Wall the Picts from Caledonia continued their incursions deep into English territory. A great movement of European tribes and nations had begun. This is the 'folk-wandering' or 'Migration' period, the 'Dark Ages', or the 'Early Christian' period. Its limiting dates in Scotland are approximately the 5th century–11th century, the period between the end of the Roman occupation and the onset of the Middle Ages.

In this time of troubles the Christian Church was the sole enduring institution. It inherited the unifying and stabilising power of the declining Empire, and it provided an ideology superior to national boundaries. The abundance in Scotland of surviving Christian crosses and cross-slabs, presumptive evidence of a greater original number, is ample testimony of the courage, pertinacity, and faith, of the Early Christians in the face of adversity. It is more: it is a heritage of works of art which is distinctive, in some ways unique, and of the highest artistic merit.

Christianity was introduced into Britain during the Roman occupation. That there was an organised church at an early date can be inferred from a record of the presence of 3 English bishops at a church council at Arles in 314. But it was not until the 5th century that the Church made a purposeful attempt to convert the Celtic West.

The process of conversion was slow and attended by many reverses: the conversion of whole communities, spectacular though it could be, and often was, could not have been deep-rooted. Even to the converted

Christianity must have been a strange and foreign faith imperfectly comprehended, where pagan gods and customs had so recently prevailed. Relapses into paganism were frequent. Fifty years after St. Augustine's landing in 597 a Kentish King could order the destruction of idols, and 50 years after that penalties were imposed for heathen worship. St. Patrick, in a letter written c. 435, castigates the chieftain Coroticus, denounces the 'apostate Picts', and refers to the betrayal of Christians into the hands of Scots and Picts.

In such societies and circumstances Christian priests and monks played an influential part. They had considerable political and cultural importance. Their leaders were frequently high-born. They were closely associated with the chieftains who most readily accepted Christianity and imposed it upon their people. By peaceful penetration they carried the Christian message into hostile territory.

Relations between pagan and Christian, between the incoming missionary and the native, would not always be violent or even antagonistic. Although the teaching of the missionary might not readily be accepted, he and his disciples would be allowed to settle and evangelise. For long Christian and heathen practices would persist together. To quicken interest and ensure goodwill the Church refrained from destroying heathen idols and temples. A letter from Pope Gregory to Abbot Mellitus, c. 600, for St. Augustine, cautions him against such destruction and exhorts him to convert the heathen customs to the true faith.

In 597, by the mission of St. Augustine to Kent, the Roman Church was formally established in England, but long before this, c. 400, St. Ninian, from his Celtic monastery at Whithorn, was evangelising the Southern Picts, and after him, in 565, Columba ventured from Ireland to the Irish Kingdom of Dalriada (the modern Argyll), to found the famous Irish monastery of Iona. From Iona in 635 Irish Celtic monks went to Northumbria by invitation of a Northumbrian King who had once sought refuge there, and, in course of time, Northumbria was the meeting place of the expanding Celtic and Roman Churches. These two churches differed fundamentally in points of organisation and observance, for the severance of the Celtic West from the Continent, by the barbarian invasions, caused the Celtic Church to develop in isolation not wholly in step with the Church of Rome. At Whitby, in 664, the disunity was resolved, to the disadvantage of the Celtic Church. Its power declined: it withdrew to the West from which it had emerged. When the Pictish nation in 710, and Iona in 716, adopted the orthodox Roman form of organisation, discipline and liturgy, the days of the Celtic Church were numbered. Yet its influence endured, particularly in art.

Little is known about St. Ninian. His nearest biographer, Bede, writing 300 years after his death, relates that the Southern Picts, renouncing idolatry, had accepted the true faith at the preaching of Ninian, a most reverend Bishop and holy man of the British nation.

A Celtic monastery such as he and Columba founded was a loosely organised assemblage of chapels and domestic buildings surrounded by a protective wall. In the enclosed area would be erected wood or stone commemorative crosses. Such monuments were erected outside also, to mark preaching stations, ecclesiastical boundaries, or the burial places of notable clerics and laymen, for at this early date the pagan customs of private burial continued, even among the converted. A schematic plan of the monastery of St. Mullins, in the 8th century Book of Mulling, shows standing crosses round a circular enclosure. Four are dedicated to the Evangelists, four to the Prophets. Within the enclosure are others, dedicated to Christ, the Apostles, and the Holy Spirit.

Apart then from the artistic merit of our early stones, which is considerable, we may expect to find in them a reflection of the influences at work in the period: pagan and Christian; Roman, Celtic, and native Pictish. The stones are known collectively as Early Christian because they belong to the Early Christian period, but some, the so-called symbol stones, may be wholly pagan. Some authorities maintain that all are Christian.

The Whithorn Stones

The earliest known Christian memorial in Scotland is an inscribed stone at Whithorn. This is the 'Latinus Stone' of c. A.D. 450 (Plate 1). It follows the contemporary Continental custom, still practised today, of recording the name of the surviving relative who erected it. Two at nearby Kirkmadrine are 6th century, a third is c. 600, according to the form of the letters employed in their inscriptions and to the style of their epitaphs. This Whithorn group of inscribed stones and a few others of like character, all occurring south of the Forth, bear witness to Roman culture in their epigraphy. They are usually ascribed to the continuing mission of Ninian, and they form a group in themselves.

Later stones at Whithorn, of the 8th century, are noticeably different from their precursors. They have strong Northumbrian art characteristics. The most notable is the inscribed St. Peter Stone of 7th or early 8th century date (Plate 1). A fragmentary cross-shaft with figure panels is Northumbrian work also, of the date of the known visit of Bishop Eardulf in 880.

The style of these and others proclaims the supremacy of the Northumbrian Church in the Lowlands at this period and supports literary evidence. Bede in his History of the English Church, written c. 731, says, 'the Pictish people are at this time also at peace with the English nation'. There were English (i.e. Northumbrian) monasteries at Whithorn, St. Andrews, Abercorn, Jedburgh and Melrose. Northumbrian work is found in all these districts. The famous Ruthwell Cross, of c. 650, one of the finest Early Christian monuments in Europe, is pure Northumbrian work. Northumbrian motifs, notably the vine-scroll, are evident elsewhere; the fantastic beast which steps through the convolutions of its own elongated body, as at Meigle and Aberlemno, is derived from the illuminated pages of the Lindisfarne Gospels of c. 700.

But the distribution of the main body of the Early Christian monuments of Scotland is north of the Forth, on the east, as far as Shetland. This coincides exactly with the area known historically to have been that of settled Pictish rule. Two main types of monument occur in this area: symbol stones, and cross-slabs.

The Pictish Symbol Stones

Little is known about the Picts, and the symbol stones attributed to them are as enigmatic as the racial history is obscure. They are graven, or sculptured in low relief, upon upright stone slabs and unshapen boulders. They have also been found as decoration on a silver pin, a silver chain, a small silver plaque, and upon bone and a few small pieces of stone.

There are 14 different symbols and they are used over and over again. They never occur singly: as many as four or five may occur together: some combinations never occur: the crescent may be crossed with a V-shaped floriated rod but never with a Z-rod; the double disc may be crossed with a Z-rod, never a V-rod: the rods never occur alone and they never occur on certain symbols: they seem to have had a subsidiary or qualifying significance affecting the meaning of the associated symbol. The most frequent symbols are the double discs and Z-rod, the crescent and V-rod. The serpent is frequent, so is the fantastic animal or "elephant". Some are not frequent.

Most of the symbols are abstract designs. Possibly some represent real objects: if so, they are so stylised as to bear little resemblance to the originals. Two or three are indeed recognisable: the comb and comb-case, the mirror, serpent, anvil and hammer.

The symbols may have been painted on bone, stone, leather and wood, and worked in coloured enamel upon metal. The stone carvings may have been painted also, as is suggested by the low relief carving and shallow incisions of some which are difficult to read (e.g.: the granite example in Elgin Cathedral). But it is not known whether they were painted or not, nor why they were made, nor anything about them whatever. In meaning and origin they are alike an enigma. They occur nowhere else in the world. They demonstrate no artistic or cultural antecedents; they come down to us widespread and mature, obviously of great and instant significance in their day. In meaning and purpose a mystery, yet artistically they are completely satisfying.

Certain boldly incised animals are frequently associated with the symbols—the fish, serpent, eagle, duck, bull, wolf or hound, stag, boar and deer. Although conventionalised, the animals are full of vitality, and executed, as the symbols are, with great ability and the utmost economy of line. (Front cover, and Plates 3, 6, 7, etc.)

There is no characteristic feature by which the symbol stones can with confidence be closely dated although the curvilinear ornamentation which frequently fills the spaces within the outline of the symbols, and the art style of the single animals, suggest a late 7th–8th century date, by parallels occurring in illuminated Gospel books, such as the Book of Kells and the Lindisfarne Gospels.

Whether or not the symbols are of pagan origin and meaning is disputable. Artistically and symbolically they are non-Christian. Only the fish is a Christian symbol[1], and it seems not to be so used upon these

[1] The first dated example is in the Catacombs of Rome, A.D. 234. It was popular in the first centuries A.D. less as from the fourth century. It occurs 13 times on Scottish Early Christian monuments. The symbol means 'Christ', from a sacred acrostic derived from the initial letters of the five Greek words for 'Jesus Christ Son of God; Saviour', which when read together give the Greek word for fish.

stones, occurring as it does in like manner to the duck, boar, hound, etc., of no Christian religious significance.

They seem to have a memorial significance and to be religious. Their prevalent occurrence upon monumental stones strongly suggests as much. They may be symbols of a pagan idolatry. But this prevalence may be fortuitous and misleading. They may have been as commonly worked on less durable material; on wood, bone, leather, metal. They may be secular: identification marks, badges of rank, indicators of social status. This would explain their occurrence upon the few small secular objects, and would explain also their non-Christian character while permitting them to be the work of Christians. The Birsay Stone (Plate 7) is perhaps significant in this connection. It has three symbols and three warriors, one pre-eminent. It was found at the head of a triple grave. This is unique, and the most important association of a symbol stone with a grave so far discovered. The symbols may describe the dead.

There is an historical argument for their being Christian, thus: the expulsion of the Celtic clergy (in favour of the Roman) from Nechtan's Pictish court in the early 8th century proves the Christianity of Nechtan at the end of the 7th century and suggests it could be earlier: if Scotland were Christianised by the end of the 7th century the symbols, if pagan and religious, must be before that date, for they would hardly be tolerated in a Christian context: with the Ninianic mission continuing from *c.* 400 and the Columban from 565 there is a likelihood of the evangelised parts of Scotland being at least nominally Christian by say 600: if Christianity proscribed the Pictish symbols they must therefore be earlier than *c.* 600 generally and earlier than *c.* 400 and 565 in areas quickly converted. This argument gives the symbols an awkwardly early end, for the succeeding 'transitional' type of monument, the cross-slab with symbols, begins at earliest in the late 7th century, probably in the 8th.

It is however arguable that pagan symbols *would* persist after the conversion, adopted and sanctified on the lines indicated by Pope Gregory's letter, in accordance with the Church's policy of reconciling pagan customs with Christian practice by sanctifying the pagan element, or during a relapse into paganism.

Thus the symbols might be pagan when occurring without the Cross, converted pagan when with it, and eventually to be dropped from the artist's repertory altogether. Two stones illustrated here suggest, by a marked difference in technique, the later addition to a symbol-stone of a composition dominated by a cross: the Glamis Stone (Plates 5, 6) which bears incised symbols on the uneven undressed surface of one side has a powerful interlaced cross in bold relief on the flat dressed surface of the other: Meigle stone 5 (Plates 39, 40) has a discrepancy in the placing of its carving which is best explained by supposing the cross to be an addition or a re-working of an older carved surface. (Re-working would also explain the unusually deep relief of the cross-bearing side.)

The Cross-Slabs

The cross-slabs are shaped, well-finished although not always regular, and made to stand erect: on them the cross assumes the first importance. It is of the type known as Celtic. It has hollows at the intersections of the four limbs and the arms are frequently connected by a 'ring of glory'[1]. Its surface is generally covered with incised or low relief interlace and its kindred systems of fretwork, scrolls and spirals. The ribbons or strands of the complicated patterns frequently begin, end, and intersect in the form of beast-heads, long snouts, or interlacing animal legs closely paralleled in the illuminated manuscripts of the 7th and 8th centuries, as are the interlaced snouted creatures which confront each other at Aberlemno, Meigle and elsewhere. The interlace is manipulated with great variety, vigour and skill. Connected series of patterns retain something of the panelled effect characteristic of the abstract and geometrical tendency of Celtic art (e.g. the Highland tartans). The panels are not necessarily symmetrical, but are balanced. They may be definite, or arbitrary, clearly separated by marginal lines, or more subtly by changes in the pattern or rhythm of the interlace, or the grouping of subject-matter. The cross is usually of the long-shafted Latin type, but the equal-armed Greek cross occurs, and often the panels of interlace upon the shaft of a long cross are contrived to produce the effect of an equal-armed cross with a downward extension of the shaft, as though the shaft were a base upon which an equal-armed cross were standing.

Fanciful animals, human figures, pictorial scenes suggesting pagan mythology, and horsemen, singly or in groups, armed for the chase or

[1] The ring is structural as well as symbolic, to support the heavy arms of a standing cross (e.g. pl. 25).

for war, are all added to the terse Pictish symbolism. Scenes drawn from early Christian imagery illustrate the symbolism of the Cross and convey to the faithful the essential ideas of Christianity: Daniel in the Lion's Den, Jonah and the Whale, the Breaking of Bread by Saints Paul and Anthony are represented more than once. These sculptures are executed with great spirit, lively movement and, at their best, with superb technical ability, particularly evident wherever horsemen are featured, and they often are, as though this were a huntsman's art. Indeed, we feel that the sculptors enjoyed their cavalcades, horsemen, and hunting scenes, but merely copied Christian subject-matter. Its range is limited (it does not include the Crucifixion) and rarely achieves the grandeur of the Saints Paul and Anthony theme on the Nigg Stone or of David, as the prefiguration of Christ, rending the lion's jaws on the St. Andrews sarcophagus. The front panel of this sarcophagus is extremely interesting in this respect, apart from its merits as a work of art. Imposing as David is he has been pushed to one side.

This sarcophagus is unique, and one of our greatest treasures. The front panel, illustrated here (Plates 20, 21) ranks among the finest examples of Dark Age Art in Europe.

There is no stereotyped arrangement of the subject-matter of the cross-slabs. On the Rossie Priory Stone (Plate 13) the hunting scene over-rides the cross and horsemen occupy the panels of the lower limb. This exemplifies a curious and telling spatial quality in the composition which is evident also on other stones, such as the St. Andrews sarcophagus, and at Meigle No. 1 (Plate 29) where horsemen, symbols, and other motifs are disposed diagonally across the stone, conveying the same impression of movement and space.

'Though the details of these diagrammatic human figures are treated in a conventional manner, there can be no doubt that the costume, the weapons, and other accessories, are those of the country and the time. In this aspect of their character, as illustrative materials of unwritten history they are as valuable as the seals and the monumental effigies of later times. They illustrate the most ancient life in Scotland of which we have any illustrations. They show it in its common as well as in its ecclesiastical and military aspects. They exhibit the dress of the huntsman, the warrior, the pilgrim, and the ecclesiastic. They furnish representations of the forms of the chariot, and the ship, the housings and harness of horses, instruments of music, arms of offence and defence, the staff of the pilgrim and the crosier of the ecclesiastic. Such implements and weapons of the period as the axe, the knife, the dirk, the sword, the spear, the shield, the bow, and the cross-bow[1], are all represented, and, so far as I know, no other representations of them exist. Customs and fashions of which there is no other distinct evidence are also represented. For instance, we learn from a comparison of all the different representations that the horsemen of that period rode without spurs or stirrups, cropped the manes and tails of their horses, used snaffle-bridles with cheek rings and ornamental rosettes, and sat upon peaked saddle-cloths; that, when journeying on horseback, they wore peaked hoods and cloaks, and when hunting or on horseback, armed, they wore a kilt-like dress, falling below mid-thighs, and a plaid across the shoulders; that they used long-bows in war, and cross-bows in hunting, that their swords were long, broad-bladed, double-edged, obtusely pointed weapons with triangular pommels and straight guards; that their spears had large lozenge-shaped heads, while their bucklers were round and furnished with bosses; that they fought on foot with sword and buckler, and on horseback with sword, spear, and shield; that when journeying on foot they wore trews or tight-fitting nether-garments, and a plaid loosely wrapped round the body, or a tight jerkin with sleeves, and belt round the waist; that they wore their hair long, flowing, and curly, sometimes with peaked beards, at other times with moustaches on the upper lip and shaven cheeks and chin; that they used covered chariots or two-wheeled carriages with poles for draught by two horses, the driver sitting on a seat over the pole, the wheels having ornamental spokes; that they used chairs with side-arms and high, curved backs, sometimes ornamented with heads of animals; that their boats had high prows and stern-posts; that the long dresses of the ecclesiastics were richly embroidered; that they walked in loose short boots, and carried crosiers and book-satchels. Such illustrations of the life and habits, the arts and industry, the costume and arms of the Celtic inhabitants of Scotland are nowhere else to be found.[2]

The achievements of the Pictish sculptors present a unique contribution to European art. The particular independent genius of these artists resides in their mastery of both closed and open composition, and an

[1]The identification of the cross-bow is disputable, as the writer of this passage admitted.

[2]Joseph Anderson: 'Scotland in Early Christian Times,' 1881, Second Series, pp. 122-125.

instinctive urge to pattern-making to which even the Cross and other Christian themes are frequently subordinated. Control of unexpectedly violent conjunctions of diverse themes is another characteristic. The vitality and freshness, and the communication of the artist's enthusiasm and familiarity with his subject enliven the spirited horsemen who step out so blithely across the sheets of stone. The hunting scenes are rendered with great precision and delicacy, and they demonstrate command of open composition with movement. On the other hand the strict and unfaltering control of interlace of remarkable complexity proves the highest technical skill combined with a notable aptitude for changing pattern.

Equally remarkable and revealing is the sculptor's attitude to his material. He takes the stone as it comes to hand, respects its shape and surfaces and refrains from ironing it flat. Unevenness is welcomed (even an interlaced cross in high relief can undulate) and fractures, holes, and other faults are accepted. They are exploited to influence the design or are boldly ignored and make their own contribution. See on the Glamis Stone (Plate 6) how the symbols are placed, and observe the importance of the natural irregularities in the general effect. See too on the Papil Stone (Plate 4) and on the Easterton of Roseisle Stone (Plate 3) how faults are accepted and not avoided, and how successfully they add interest and life to the figures.

These stones are the national monuments of the Picts, and an astonishing manifestation of their genius. In beholding them and in recognising the details of their apparel and accoutrements we are as near to the Picts as one can be, or is ever likely to be.

The High Crosses

The monastery of Iona was an Irish foundation, and throughout the 7th and 8th centuries continued to be peopled by Irishmen ('Scotti'). In front of the mediaeval abbey church there stand today two wheeled High Crosses, dedicated to St. John and St. Martin (Plate 24). The cross is of the same form as that sculptured upon the slabs but it is now freed from the slab and stands upon a high stone base, and the arms are wheeled by the 'ring of glory'. All sides are covered with an exuberance of interlacing, spirals, and the like.

Worked into these close-knit and complicated patterns are scriptural scenes.

These crosses are intensely Celtic. There are no Pictish motifs; no symbols; no Pictish horsemen. They occur nowhere in the Pictish area, but in the west country only, and in Ireland. The beautiful Kildalton Cross on Islay (Plate 25) is the only other to survive complete, although for Iona sundry detached and broken parts, and a legend, testify to the existence of many in Celtic times. They lack the enigmatic interest of the cross-slabs, but they are of rare beauty, and they have with the symbol stones and cross-slabs a special uniqueness in the world of art. Outside the Celtic West they are not found in the art of any other people at any time. And yet they are the products of what we call the Dark Ages. The modern artist does not disdain to turn to them for inspiration: they are the originals of the innumerable Celtic crosses, which, as gravestones and war memorials, are still erected in our church-yards and roadways throughout Scotland. Debased and commercialised they are turned out by the thousand every year as best-selling souvenirs.

The Dating of the Monuments

The three main classes may each be sub-divided, according to their art style, iconography, and the relevant political and ecclesiastical history. In the analysis of these diverse elements and in the conclusions conse-quently drawn from them there is considerable disagreement among authorities and no close dating is yet possible. The following dates are given as feasible central dates for the life of each main type:

> Pictish symbol stones: 7th century
> Pictish cross-slabs: 8th century
> High Crosses: 9th or 10th century

The Meigle Stones

THERE are some five hundred Early Christian Stones of all types still in existence in Scotland. Many stand in their presumed original position, or near to it. Some are in private ownership, others are in local museums. The National Museum of Antiquities in Edinburgh has a splendid collection and an extensive series of casts of specimens not in the collection. The Ministry of Public Building and Works has many single stones in its guardianship and four important collections: at *Whithorn Priory* in Wigtownshire, described in the official guide-book to that monument (see Bibliography), at *St Andrews Cathedral*, Fife, described in the cathedral museum, and at *Meigle*, Perthshire, and *St. Vigeans* near Arbroath, which are described in detail below.

The Meigle Museum was a schoolhouse. It was acquired by public subscription through the exertions of Sir George Kinloch, Bart. at the end of the last century. In 1936 the museum and the collection were made over to the Minister of Works. In 1949 the museum was renovated and the stones were re-arranged. The number for each item in the following catalogue is that in the standard reference book, the great and definitive work by Romilly Allen and Anderson (see Bibliography).

2. Upright cross-slab. The small projections on sides and top are of unknown purpose and meaning. The 'ring of glory' contains an equal-armed cross: both are embellished with raised bosses, 33 altogether, possibly inspired by the rivet heads of contemporary metal work. The surfaces of cross and wheel have been covered with a diagonal key pattern. The long shaft has three pairs of facing beasts. On the left of the shaft are three climbing figures, the top kneels and hauls below it, a gesture of muscular action which is quite uncharacteristic of our Early Christian art: on the right of the shaft three beasts with large heads and long coiled bodies. The central subject on the other side is Daniel in the Lion's Den symbolising the delivery of the faithful from the power of evil. It has an early history, first occurring in the 2nd and 3rd century in the Catacombs. It occurs on seven crosses in Ireland and six in Scotland. Daniel's arms are raised in the 'orans' or ancient attitude of prayer as he stands appealingly in the midst of fierce lions. Above Daniel is a superb equestrian group quite classical in conception and execution. The top figure is cloaked, bearded, carries a spear and is girt with a sword. He sits upon a saddle-cloth; his horse is bridled. In front of him are two hounds with an angel above probably representing the Soul as it did in mediaeval art. Beneath him a cavalcade is suggested, as on a classical frieze, by three closely set riders abreast, followed by a single rider. Below Daniel, a centaur with two axes and a branch of a tree. At the bottom, a man with a club, and a dragon grasping a horned beast by the nose.

This magnificent monument dominates the museum. It seems to vibrate, and the effect is enhanced by the different colours of the stone.

The subject matter is a notable combination of native-and-foreign and pagan-and-Christian ideas. The realistic and spirited horsemen are characteristically 'Pictish', the centaur and Daniel are faithfully reproduced borrowings from foreign sources: the centaur is a pagan motif, Daniel is Christian. (Plates 26, 27): see Daniel also on St. Vigeans No. 14.

1. Upright cross-slab: the cross is enriched by seven linked panels of interlace, the arms are hollowed at the intersections and each hollow is spanned by a raised quarter circle, recalling the nimbus or ring of glory of No. 2 and the wheeled High Crosses of Iona and Ireland.

The background to the cross contains beasts only, real and fabulous. At the top, two snouted boar-like animals; on the left, a beast with goat's horns, a snouted beast with long spiral body and a sea-horse and hippocamp facing one another; on the right, a pair of interlaced sea-horses and a horned animal with a long tail ending in open jaws which bite a snouted serpent. (Plate 28)

The back of the slab is treated as a single field for sculpture. The upper half has six symbols; fish, beast-head, triquetra, 'elephant,' serpent and Z-rod, mirror-and-comb; the lower half, a kneeling camel, five horsemen and a hound, an angel and a beast with coiled body. The upward diagonal movement, sustained throughout the composition, is remarkable. The horsemen seem to be on the move and without restriction. So freely and purposefully do they cross the sheet of stone that the onlooker is tempted to walk round to the other side to see if there are more. The diagonal movement is emphasised by the placing of the mirror, comb and camel and by the serpent and Z-rod above them. The great size of the fish, stretching right across the page, is just right, steadying the composition, and pulling it together just where it is likely to get out of control. (Plate 29)

This seems to be a re-used prehistoric monument. The base or socket bears 'cup-marks' such as are found upon Standing Stones of the Bronze Age (approximately 2000 B.C.–approximately 500 B.C.). As these are invisible a plaster cast of the cup-marked area has been made. It stands against the wall nearby. (A4)

4. Upright cross-slab; central part conjectural. The cross is divided into panels of differing interlace. On either side of the cross-head a long necked snouted beast bites the neck of a marginal beast. The marginal beasts have each a long claw and they face each other, snout to snout, over the top of the cross. These marginal beasts occur on other stones and sometimes continue all round but do not appear to have done so here. On the left of the shaft is a horned beast with convoluted body: on the right a bearded man with long Pictish hair seizes a rearing horse by its forelegs. On either side of the bottom was a panel of interlaced serpents; the heads can be seen at

the bottom of the left-hand panel, the tails in the right-hand panel. Note the subtlety of the carving, the sculptor's sympathetic handling of his stone. The undulations are not ironed out, not even for the cross. (see p. 16)

On the other side, a Pictish horseman, bearded, and with long curling hair, armed with sword and spear; reins and saddlecloth evident, no signs of stirrups: note that the spear and details of horse trappings are in very low relief, or incised. Behind the horseman two interlaced serpents with long snouts grasp one another by the tail. Below this, a smaller Pictish horseman, a quadruped biting a complicated serpent, the elephant symbol and the crescent and V-rod. At the bottom, grotesque beasts worked into an intricate flowing pattern of interlace. That on the left seems to be a gryphon; its forefeet are clawed and birdlike, the back feet are hoofed, the tail is snouted and bites the wing. (Plates 30, 31)

11. Recumbent grave-stone: on one side a procession of three Pictish horsemen, the foremost attended by a small hound. Movement is suggested by the diminishing size of the cavalcade and the spritely modelling of the horses' legs. In the rear, a dancing man with a beast's head. He grasps two serpents, one by the neck in his hand, the other is in his mouth. The raised margin of this sunken panel has been richly decorated.

On the other side are four panels of ornament; on the left, two interlaced beasts; next, a group of two beasts, a panel of twelve raised bosses linked by interlace work, and at the head seven bosses of escaping spirals within a circle on each side of which is a grotesque beast. At the top is a man lying with his head in the mouth of the beast on the right and his legs in the mouth of that on the left. The raised margins of this side are decorated also.

The large end or head of the stone has been covered with interlace but not the smaller or rear end. The square recess in the rear end is of uncertain date and purpose. It seems to be modern yet the tooling is not and the surface is quite unlike the mutilated upper surface of the stone. At the head of the upper surface is part of a socket for a small cross. (Plate 32)

12. Recumbent grave-stone: on the upper surface, two narrow margins of interlaced work, a row of recessed diamond shapes, and the socket of a small upright cross. On one side, a fish monster with long serpentine body and fins; on the other, a stag with a beast biting one of its legs and two bulls. (Plate 33)

26. Recumbent grave-stone: slotted on the upper surface for an upright cross. The shaft would apparently have been held secure by two marginal beasts, whose open mouths would appear to grasp it. The beasts have large heads and fangs in both top and bottom jaws. Their bodies die away into a margin of interlace and re-appear at the other end as long beaked creatures confronting one another as on stone No. 4. The upper surface has three panels. At the head, three coiled serpents, in the centre, twelve bosses with escaping spirals, at the foot, two linked sea-horses. On one long side, a pair of beasts (? bears) devour or disgorge a man's body, a leg appears in the mouth of one, the severed head above; in the middle of this side is a human swastika (this motif occurs on several Irish crosses and in the Book of Kells) and at the right-hand end, a bear and a horse. On the other side: bear-like and bird-like creatures with spiralled and interlaced tails: the centre-piece is a square key pattern, then five horsemen (three close-set abreast as on stone No. 2) and two running hounds. At the head end of the stone a quadruped with a human head pursues a naked Pict looking apprehensively over his shoulder. This beast may be a Manticora, a fabulous creature of frequent occurrence in twelfth and thirteenth century art. (Plates 35-38)

5. Small upright cross-slab: border of interlace contains equal-armed cross upon ornamental base. The arms of the cross are covered with fret-work and key-pattern, the centre with spirals. The angles at the inter-sections are hollowed as on No. 1, and the hollows have contained each a cluster of three small bosses of escaping spiral decoration. The base is ornamented with circular interlace and two splendid animal heads. The panels of the background are inhabited by a grotesque beast; that on the bottom right is a bird swallowing a serpent.

On the other face of the stone is the lower part of a horseman who wears shoes with pointed heels; reins and saddle-cloth are evident, the horse's tail is cropped. On one of the sides is the mirror symbol and below it the 'elephant' both incised. These Pictish symbols and the Pictish horseman occupy the same extent of the stone (from top to bottom) and leave below them a rough unworked area, but the sculpture of the cross-bearing side is more extensive, it occupies the whole side. This suggests that the stone was originally horseman and symbol only, and that it was originally buried up to about the bottom of these motifs, to be lifted later to receive the cross, and then set up a second time, leaving exposed on the other sides the base which was meant to be buried. (Plates 39, 40)

23. Upright cross-slab: on the front, a long-shafted cross with 'ring of glory', a little figure on each side. On the back two fanciful beasts with long interlaced necks, and a pair of beasts with a single head.

22. Slab: in the middle a triton, mermaid, or celtic god with a double interlacing fish-tail. The figure holds long coils of hair: on either side a ? bear and a dog (otter?). The 'bear' seems to have bridle and bit, but the lines suggesting this may be purely decorative. (Plate 41).

3. Upper part of upright cross-slab: decorated cross: on the left of the shaft the top of the double-disc symbol: on the other side, a horseman wearing pointed shoes, armed with spear and sword. Note reins, bridle and saddle-cloth. (Plate 34)

25. Recumbent hog-backed grave-stone: the thick decorated ridge ends in a beast's head, as though the ridge were itself a snake-like creature: the sides are worked in three rows of scales or tiles. Note the beautiful model-ling of the body, undulating yet firm, instantly recalling the body of a fish or animal, the sculptor respecting the shape of the stone as it came to his hands. (Plate 42: see No. 4 and p. 16)

9. Recumbent grave-stone: on one side are five panels, at the head a beast, then a bird seizing a man by the neck, both interlaced; an elongated beast, a panel of spiral work, traces of two men. On the other side are four panels: at the foot, a gryphon carrying an animal interlaced; a beast interlaced in its own body, and a pair of facing animals with a single head. The upper surface is slotted for an upright cross.

7. Upper part of upright cross-slab. The head has key pattern; on either side a crouching man and a dragon-like animal. On the back, the double-disc and Z-rod, part of a comb symbol (bottom left).

27. Cross-slab: front part of shaft has spirals: interlace on the left. On the back, two enthroned clerics (? SS. Paul and Anthony breaking bread) and a small crouching figure with pointed beard and drooping moustache.

6. Middle of cross-slab. The shaft has fretwork. Borders of key pattern enclose a horseman armed with a round shield, sword and spear. Below the horseman are the double-disc and crescent symbols; at the bottom, a hound.

28. Cross-slab: lower end of a cross-shaft devoid of ornament, surrounding it is key pattern and spiral-work.

29. Part of cross-slab, two clerics and a crosier: robes enriched with interlace. The figure on the right has a circular brooch high up on each breast.

20. Part of a panel with key pattern. Horseman on other side.

15. Lower part of upright cross-slab: the bottom of the shaft has interlace: on the left, two beasts bite each other: on the right, a beast bites its back.

8. Fragment of small cross-slab with what might be a symbol or a stylised object, represented by a circular ring attached to two horizontal bars crossed by a shorter vertical bar. Below this are the heads of two facing beasts, their paws in each others mouths. Cross head on other side.

30. Part of a serpent.

21. Cross-slab: long-shafted cross decorated with circular interlace and key pattern.

A1. Two robed clerics, with books. The fringes of the robes are decorated with Greek key pattern. (Additional to Romilly Allen and Anderson).

A2. Small equal-armed cross with hollowed intersections of the arms. The margin has interlace. (Additional to Romilly Allen and Anderson).

A3. One limb of a cross, below it a panel ornamented with C-scrolls (cf. No. 13). (Additional to Romilly Allen and Anderson).

A4. Plaster cast of cup-marked base of No. 1 (see under No. 1). (Additional to Romilly Allen and Anderson).

The St. Vigeans Stones

THE stones in this collection come from the church on the hill nearby. As we see the church today it is a nineteenth century building, but it incorporates ancient masonry in its fabric. The place-name and the monuments prove that there was an Early Christian settlement here which was founded by St. Fechin[1] or by one of his followers in his name. In the course of time which has since elapsed, during which the church has been enlarged and rebuilt more than once, many similar commemorative monuments have presumably been lost. The survivors have suffered through misuse and neglect. When the present church was erected in 1872 some were built into its walls, some were exhibited in the porch and others were housed in a chamber in the tower. One (No. 29) was recently upon the lintel of the doorway in the manse garden wall, after long use as a step in the churchyard.

Such was the state of a collection none the less renowned in the Early Christian archaeology of Scotland when in 1960 the Ministry of Public Building and Works, in co-operation with the minister of the church and its congregation, removed the stones from their various situations and placed them in an unused cottage which had been presented to the Ministry for conversion to a museum in which they could be suitably exhibited after repair. They have been arranged according to type, with explanatory remarks and drawings to assist the visitor. The following is a descriptive catalogue of each item. The item numbers, as in the Meigle catalogue, are those of the great and definitive work on the subject by Romilly Allen and Anderson (see Bibliography).

1. 'The Drosten Stone'. Upright cross-slab. Particularly well-known because of the inscription at the bottom of one of the narrow sides. It is not an important inscription as far as its message goes, but inscriptions are rare and appear to be in an unknown language. In later ninth-century script three names are given, and one can say little more than that, save

[1] St. Fechin was Irish. He died in Ireland in 644. The name Ecclefechan commemorates him also. The name St. Vigeans comes from Vigianus, the latin form of Fechin.

23

that they are Drosten, Uoret and Forcus, seemingly Pictish names rendered in Gaelic. It reads thus:

drosten
ipeuoret
ettfor
cus

i.e. Drosten ipe Uoret ett Forcus. The word ipe is quite unknown. Perhaps a memorial to the people named. It might not be significant, but it is worth noting here, that there are three Pictish symbols on this stone. They might allude to those three people. We suggest such a connection on the Birsay Stone also (p. 12 and Plate 7), where three Pictish warriors are drawn beneath three symbols. There is no inscription on the Birsay Stone, but there might have been. It is incomplete. (See also No. 4).

The front face of the slab bears a cross which occupies most of it. The cross is decorated all over with interlace or knotwork. In the top left-hand corner is a little winged angel or 'soul' figure. On the left of the shaft, at the top, is an extended animal seen from above. Its neck and head seem to have been stretched and bent round to lie against its left side. It has a long tail with a snouted head interlaced with and biting a serpentile creature below it. This creature has a larger head, also biting. At the bottom of this panel is a long-necked winged dragon whose tail is twisted through its rear legs. On the right of the shaft, at the top, is a probably winged beast with a long neck, below it a snarling creature with claws, then a beast with three sets of bristles or humps (a dromedary?), and at the bottom a pair of interlaced serpents.

On the other side, at the top, is a hunt; two hounds in full pursuit of a stag: also a small animal and parts of others (behind the stag a bird?). Below this scene are the three symbols referred to, the double-disc and Z-rod, the crescent, and on the right of the crescent the mirror and comb. The lower part of this side has a group of animals; a bear, a hind suckling its young, a creature with tail between its legs, looking up, an eagle as a bird of prey upon a fish, and a beast with a large curved horn on its head (unicorn?). At the bottom a cloaked Pictish archer aims at a well-tusked boar.

The narrow sides bear interlace and foliage. The interlace above the inscription is characteristically Pictish (see the cross-shaft), but the trailing vine-leaf on the other narrow side is not Pictish but is characteristic of Anglian or Northumbrian sculpture of the later ninth century. The inscription and the art style of this stone therefore agree to date it approximately to the period 850-900 A.D. It is probably nearer 850.

This stone was recovered in two broken parts, recently united. It is still incomplete, as can be seen. (Plates 46 and 47).

2. Cross-slab, top and back missing. The front face has a cross-shaft treated in three ornamental panels, of interlace, diagonal fretwork or key pattern, and scrolls or spiral pattern. On the left of the shaft is a part of the mirror symbol, on the right the serpent and Z-rod, below it the bird or eagle. This stone is much worn, perhaps in some late re-use as a threshold.

3. Part of a double-disc and Z-rod.

4. Fragment of top of an upright cross-slab. On one side, the top left-hand corner of the front, there is part of the cross and the top left-hand quadrant of the ring which connected the arms (the 'ring of glory'). In the corner a triquetra knot. On the other side, the top right-hand corner of the back of the slab, there is a monk or priest in a peaked hood, behind him his pastoral staff or crosier and the double-disc symbol. It is interesting to note this association of the double-disc, the crosier and the monkish figure. There must have been some obvious connection. (See also the ecclesiastics with symbols beside them on the upper part of the Dunfallandy stone, Plate 12, etc.).

5. Fragment of upright cross-slab sculptured on one face. At the top, lower part of a rectangular panel (bottom of a cross-shaft?). Below it the double-disc and Z-rod.

6. Fragment of upright cross-slab sculptured on two faces. On one side a panel of interlace, on the other a double-disc and part of the Z-rod. The discs are each ornamented with four raised bosses of spiralwork.

7. Upright cross-slab severely trimmed in some late re-use. On the front a long-shafted cross stands upon an oblong base (see reconstruction drawing of cross on wall in right, Plate 49). The cross has expanded arms with a central disc at the intersection, and it is decorated in panels of interlace, key patterns and spirals. The centres of the spirals on the shaft terminate in interlocking heads of men and of birds. On the left of the shaft are five figures, the one in the middle being head downwards over a rectangular block (? St. John the Evangelist in a pot of oil, as on the Glamis Stone, Plate 5). The others are cloaked and wear pointed shoes. The lower two are tonsured clerics with long cowled cloaks ornamented at the foot. Each has a staff, and one has a book satchel slung round his neck. The figures above them have looked towards each other (note their feet and the hood of the right-hand figure). They are robed and are probably monks or priests also. On the right of the shaft is a pair of enthroned robed figures holding a circular object between them. This scene probably represents SS Paul and Anthony breaking bread in the desert. Below them is a bull confronted by a naked kneeling man with rod or knife upraised to its throat. His tongue protrudes. Meaning unknown. Note the details of dress, chairs etc. on this fine work.

The other side of the slab was richly sculptured also. The head of another splendid cross can still be seen, and traces of sculpture beneath it on the left, but the surface has been grievously damaged.

The subject-matter of this magnificent memorial—it must have been seven feet high or more—is of great interest although inexplicable still. Two major crosses in elaborate high relief, each dominating one side, is itself a notable occurrence. (Plates 48 and 49).

8. Recumbent grave-stone similar to the distinctive Meigle type (Plates 32, 33, 35, 37). A frieze of beasts; on the extreme left a stag and hind are followed by a young deer. They are pursued by a dog with its tongue hanging out. At the right-hand end is a fanciful bird with elaborate stylised plumage. Has the artist not made up his mind about the blank panel? (Plate 51). The top has a cross socket and a reworked central feature.

9. High relief boss on the upper arm of a free-standing cross. (There was another boss on the back). Decoration very much weathered. The restoration drawing on the wall on the left (Plate 44) shows its position on the complete cross and reproduces the weathered patterns. The stand upon which the boss is placed has a painted full-size reproduction of the immediately adjacent parts. Note that the connecting ring of the arms is not circular, which would make for a striking if unconventional variation of the wheeled cross silhouette.

10. Upright cross-slab. It has a tenon at the foot (unseen) for the socket of its base. In the centre of the front face is an interlaced cross. On either side of the head is a long-legged winged creature with long bent neck, probably a large bird, and on either side of the shaft a panel of interlace. On the back a crescent-shaped arch of interlace encloses a pair of figures, probably seated ecclesiastics, very crudely fashioned, as are the interlace and key patterns on the narrow sides. Suggestion of animal below the figures. (Plate 50).

11. Upright cross-slab. In the middle of the front face is a wheeled cross upon a base. The expanded arms are connected by the nimbus or 'ring of glory'. On each side of the base is a robed and tonsured monk or priest; the figure on the left holds a book in his left hand and points to the page with his right (see also No. 18), above each a triquetra knot. On the other side are two seated ecclesiastics each with a book and a sceptre or flabellum (long liturgical fan) in his hand. Between and above them was a smaller robed figure whose feet and garment can just be seen. Below them two hooded figures (laymen?), each with a staff, confront one another. (Plate 45).

12. Lower part of upright cross-slab. In the centre of the front face is a cross upon an arched or hooped base, ornamented all over with interlace. It is very probable that stone No. 24 is the top left-hand corner of this slab.

13. Recumbent tombstone. On top, a rectangular recessed panel containing a wheeled cross, below it a circular medallion, a long-legged beast biting its tail, and another wheeled cross. Margin of interlace ending in beast-head.

14. Recumbent tombstone. Undecorated recessed panel in the centre of the upper surface. The panel is surrounded by a wide raised margin with interlace and running spiral. There is a socket for a smaller upright cross at the head of the upper surface. On the side, at the right, there is an incised subject, a man between two fierce beasts, probably Daniel in the Lion's Den, which is to be seen also on Meigle No. 2 (Plate 27). On the extreme right is a naked man upside down. On the left, parts of another incised scene with beasts. (Plate 51).

15. Free-standing cross with its expanded arms decorated with spiral and fretwork or key pattern: shaft restored.

16. Incomplete pillar with a cross upon a rectangular base in the centre of one face, the whole decorated with key pattern very crudely executed. This pillar was square and is known to have had a similar cross on three sides. Presumably there was another on the fourth side also.

17. Upright cross-slab. On the front face is the lower part of the head of the cross, with the lower quadrants of the connecting rings. The cross-shaft is decorated with interlace and has had on either side of it an ecclesiastic holding a book. On the back, a typical Pictish horseman.

18. Upright cross-slab. On the front face is the middle part of a cross-shaft with key pattern. On each side a serpentine creature with its tail in its mouth; the body forms a knot. On the back, part of an enthroned figure holding a book in his left hand, his right points to the page, as on stone No. 11.

19. Fragment of upright cross-slab. On one face we have the top and left arms of a cross spanned by a cable moulding which might represent the quadrant of the ring connecting the arms. There is a griffin contained in this angle. On the other side of the stone is a crouching stag with legs doubled up underneath the body.

20. Fragment with two animals, that on right is beaked and clawed, probably a griffin.

21. Fragment of upright cross-slab. On the front face there are parts of two arms of a cross with their connecting rings. On the other side of the stone is the head of a reined horse, and a single spiral above it.

22. Lower part of a cross-slab. On the front face is the bottom of a cross-shaft ornamented with fretwork or key pattern. On the back of the stone a horseman armed with a spear. (This fragment is now united with No. 23; see Plate 44).

23. The middle part of an upright cross-slab bearing a cross ornamented with fretwork or key pattern. (This fragment is now united with No. 22; see Plate 44).

24. Fragment of a cross-slab (probably No. 12) with the top arm of a cross; on the right a scroll of foliage. On the back of the stone the top arm of another cross ornamented with interlace, upper part of a beast in a sunken panel on the left.

25. Fragment. A man hanging to the neck of a horse.

26. Fragment of an upright cross-slab with scroll-work.

27. Small semicircular fragment with a single spiral.

28. A small triangular fragment with the head of a man.

29. Centre part of a recumbent tombstone. The sloping or coped top was fashioned as a tiled or slated roof with a ridge. The sides have been cut away. This stone was for long a step in the churchyard, later it lay upon the lintel of the doorway in the manse garden wall, from which situation it was moved to the museum. Note that the ridge ends in a flattened beast-head.

A1. Top corner of a cross-slab with plain cross on both sides. (Additional to Romilly Allen and Anderson).

A2. Fragment of cross-slab with interlace. (Additional to Romilly Allen and Anderson).

A3. Fragment of cross-slab (Additional to Romilly Allen and Anderson).

Plate 1: Whithorn: right centre 'Latinus Stone', left centre 'St. Peter Stone'. (pp. 9, 10)

(*Whithorn Priory Museum*)

3

Plate 2: Dunnichen symbol stone: "flower", double-disc
and Z-rod, mirror and comb.

(*Dunnichen House*)

Plate 3: Easterton of Roseisle symbol stone: goose, fish. (p. 16)
Plate 4: Papil: cross, 4 clerics, ? lion of St. Mark, bird-men. (p. 16)

(*National Museum of Antiquities*)

Plate 5: Glamis: front; cross with symbols and figures, 9 ft. high.
(pp. 3, 13)

(*The Manse, Glamis*)

Plate 6: Glamis: back; symbols only, serpent, fish (two fishes, one at top?), mirror. (pp. 3, 13, 16)

Plate 7: Birsay: 3 symbols, ? totem eagle,
3 warriors. (p. 12)

Plate 8: Invergowrie: a Pict drinks; note circular shield.

Plate 9: Aberlemno: front; cross and interlaced beasts.

(*Aberlemno churchyard*)

Plate 10: Aberlemno: back; Pictish horsemen, symbols above.

Plate 11: Dunfallandy: front; cross, beasts,
? 2 angels (from a cast in Nat. Mus. Ant.).

(*Original at Dunfallandy House, Pitlochry*)

Plate 12: Dunfallandy: back; seated ? clerics,
Pictish horseman and symbols (cast).

Plate 13: Rossie Priory: cross, Pictish hunting-scene and symbols. (p. 14)

(Rossie Priory)

Plate 14: St. Andrews Cathedral, cross-slab.

(*St. Andrews Cathedral Museum*)

Plate 15: Invergowrie: front; cross only.
(*National Museum of Antiquities*)

Plate 16: Invergowrie: back; clerics and dragons.

Plate 17: Inchbrayock: front; cross and figures.

(Montrose Museum)

Plate 18: Inchbrayock: back; Pictish hunting-scene and ? Samson
with the jaw-bone of an ass.

Plate 19: Hilton of Cadboll: huntsmen, Pictish chieftainess
(side-saddle), trumpeters, and symbols.

(National Museum of Antiquities)

Plate 20: St. Andrews Cathedral Sarcophagus
(conjectural restoration). (p. 14)

Plate: 21: detail of the above, hunting scene.

(*St. Andrews Cathedral Museum*)

Plate 22: Aberlemno: wheeled cross on slab, adoring angels with
books, interlace all over.

(*Aberlemno roadside*)

Plate 23: Dupplin: lower half, warriors, etc.; upper half, scrolls and interlace.

(*Dupplin Castle*)

Plate 24: St. Martin's Cross, Iona: a non-Pictish wheeled **High Cross**.
(p. 16)

Plate 25: Kildalton: a non-Pictish wheeled High Cross. (p. 17)

Plate 26: Meigle No. 2, front. (p. 18)

Plate 27: Meigle No. 2, back. (p. 18)

Plate 28: Meigle No. 1, front. (p. 19)

Plate 29: Meigle No. 1, back. (p. 19)

Plate 30: Meigle No. 4, front. (p. 19)

Plate 31: Meigle No. 4, back. (p. 19)

Plate 32: Meigle No. 11, side. (p. 20)

Plate 33: Meigle No. 12, side. (p. 20)

Plate 34: Meigle No. 3, back. (p. 21)

Plate 35: Meigle No. 26, side. (p. 20)

Plate 36: Detail of the above.

Plate 37: Meigle No. 26, side. (p. 20)

Plate 38: Detail of the above.

Plate 39: Meigle No. 5, front. (p. 21)

Plate 40: Meigle No. 5, side. (p. 21)

Plate 41: Meigle No. 22 (p. 21)

Plate 42: Meigle No. 25 (p. 21)

Plate 43: St. Vigeans. The cottage in the centre is the museum.

Plate 44: St. Vigeans Museum. No. 11 in left foreground, Nos. 22 and 23 (united) at the right, No. 7 in the centre.

Plate 45: St. Vigeans No. 11, back
(*for front see plate* 44)

Plate 46: St. Vigeans No. 1 'The Drosten Stone', front.

Plate 47: St. Vigeans No. 1 'The Drosten Stone', back.

Plate 48: St. Vigeans No. 7.

Plate 49: St. Vigeans No. 7. Reconstruction drawing of the cross
and its base.

Plate 50: St. Vigeans No. 10.

Plate 51: St. Vigeans No. 8 above, No. 14 below.

Bibliography

J. ROMILLY ALLEN and J. ANDERSON. *The Early Christian Monuments of Scotland.* 1903.

J. ROMILLY ALLEN. *Christian Symbolism in Great Britain and Ireland.* 1887.

J. ANDERSON. *Scotland in Early Christian Times.* 1880-1, especially the second series.

NORA K. CHADWICK. *Celtic Britain.* 1963.

O. G. S. CRAWFORD. 'The vine-scroll in Scotland', *Antiquity,* vol. XI (1937).

C. L. CURLE. 'The Chronology of the Early Christian Monuments of Scotland'—*Proceedings of the Society of Antiquaries of Scotland.* Vol. LXXIV (1939-40).

ISOBEL M. HENDERSON. 'The Origin Centre of the Pictish Symbol Stones'. *Proceedings of the Society of Antiquaries of Scotland',* vol. XCI (1957-58).

C. A. RALEGH RADFORD. 'The Early Christian Monuments of Scotland'. *Antiquity* vol. XVI (1942). *Whithorn Priory.* Official guide-book, H.M.S.O. 1957.

R. B. K. STEVENSON. 'Pictish Art', in *The Problem of the Picts,* 1955 'The Chronology and relationship of some Irish and Scottish Crosses' *Journal of Royal Society of Antiquaries of Ireland,* vol. LXXXVI, part I (1956).

J. STUART. *Sculptured Stones of Scotland.* 1856-7.

CHARLES THOMAS. 'The Animal Art of the Scottish Iron Age and its Origins', *Archaeological Journal* vol. CXVIII (1961), and 'The Interpretation of the Pictish Symbols', forthcoming in the same journal, vol. CXX (1963).

Printed in Scotland for HER MAJESTY'S STATIONERY OFFICE
by Pickering & Inglis Ltd.   Wt. 72135.   K.26

S.O. Code No. 67-112-0-64